WHERE ARE THEY?

FIND FRANKIE

By
Anthony Tallarico

kidsbooks®
Incorporated

Copyright © 1990 Kidsbooks, Inc. and Anthony Tallarico
7004 N. California Ave.
Chicago, Ill. 60645

It is the night of the Monster Club meeting. Every monster member, young and old, ugly and uglier is in attendance. The clubhouse is to be torn down and the monsters need a new place to meet. All the monsters are listening carefully—except Frankie.

FIND FRANKIE AT THE MONSTER CLUB MEETING AND...

- ☐ Arrow
- ☐ Ax
- ☐ Balloon
- ☐ Bats (4)
- ☐ Birdcage
- ☐ Bones (4)
- ☐ Broom
- ☐ Candles (7)
- ☐ Candy canes (2)
- ☐ Clothesline
- ☐ Cobweb
- ☐ Coffins (2)
- ☐ Cup
- ☐ Grapes
- ☐ Hot dog
- ☐ Jack-o'-lantern
- ☐ Mice (3)
- ☐ Nail
- ☐ Noose
- ☐ Pie
- ☐ Rabbit
- ☐ Skulls (4)
- ☐ Teddy bear
- ☐ TV set
- ☐ Voodoo doll
- ☐ Yo-yo

Suddenly...

...Frankie is lost in the outside world! There are so many sights and sounds, and so much to see. Maybe he can find a new meeting place for the monsters.

FIND FRANKIE ON THE STREET AND...

☐ Alien
☐ Bird singing
☐ Bowling ball
☐ Cat
☐ Elephant
☐ Falling flowerpot
☐ Fire hydrants (3)
☐ Flower van
☐ Football
☐ Guitar
☐ Hamburger
☐ Humpty Dumpty
☐ Karate bird
☐ King
☐ Kite
☐ Monkey
☐ Moose
☐ Mummy
☐ Ostrich
☐ Pizza
☐ Pogo stick
☐ Quicksand
☐ Rocket
☐ Santa Claus
☐ Scarecrow
☐ Tennis player
☐ Toothbrush
☐ Tuba
☐ Turtle
☐ Viking
☐ Water-skier

Frankie wonders where he should go first.

Wow! There's a lot going on in this store! Frankie can easily get lost in this dizzy, busy place.

FIND FRANKIE IN THE SUPER SUPERMARKET AND...

- ☐ Banana peel
- ☐ Basketball
- ☐ Bird
- ☐ Boat
- ☐ Bone
- ☐ Cactus
- ☐ Candles (2)
- ☐ Carrots
- ☐ Cheerleader
- ☐ Clown
- ☐ Duck
- ☐ Elephant
- ☐ "Fido"
- ☐ Fish heads
- ☐ Hammock
- ☐ Igloo
- ☐ Jack-o'-lantern
- ☐ Marshmallow
- ☐ Mermaid
- ☐ Mouse
- ☐ Periscope
- ☐ Ping-Pong ball
- ☐ Roller skates
- ☐ Six other monsters
- ☐ Skull
- ☐ Snowman
- ☐ Surfer
- ☐ Thief
- ☐ Tin Man
- ☐ Toast
- ☐ Wagon
- ☐ Witch
- ☐ Yo-yo

After all this activity, Frankie needs to find a quiet, dark place to relax.

Unfortunately, this show is so bad that even a nice monster like Frankie can't watch it for long.

FIND FRANKIE AT THE THEATER AND...

☐ Alligator
☐ Arrows (2)
☐ Camel
☐ Candle
☐ Chicken
☐ Clipboard
☐ Cowboy
☐ Deer
☐ Elephants (3)
☐ Fire hydrant
☐ Fish (4)
☐ Frog
☐ Ghosts (3)
☐ Giraffe
☐ Hammer
☐ Jack-in-the-box
☐ Jack-o'-lantern
☐ Lost shoe
☐ Mice (3)
☐ Octopus
☐ Paintbrush
☐ Peter Pan
☐ Pillow
☐ Satellite dish
☐ Snail
☐ Star
☐ Tin Man
☐ TV set
☐ Umbrellas (2)

Frankie needs some fresh air. So it's off to...

...a place where the creatures look even stranger than he does. Some have fur and some have feathers. Some have horns. Some are scary!

FIND FRANKIE AT THE ZOO AND...

- ☐ Baby taking a bath
- ☐ Balloons (6)
- ☐ Beach balls (3)
- ☐ Books (2)
- ☐ Brooms (2)
- ☐ Cactus
- ☐ Camera
- ☐ Cowboy
- ☐ Dunce cap
- ☐ Elf
- ☐ Fisherman
- ☐ Flamingo
- ☐ Ghosts (2)
- ☐ Heart
- ☐ Ice-cream cones (2)
- ☐ Kite
- ☐ Old tire
- ☐ Picnic basket
- ☐ Quarter moon
- ☐ Robin Hood
- ☐ Sailor
- ☐ Santa Claus
- ☐ Skateboard
- ☐ Socks (2)
- ☐ Stepladder
- ☐ Telescope
- ☐ Tick-tack-toe
- ☐ Trash baskets (3)
- ☐ Turtle
- ☐ Witch

After the zoo, Frankie is a little hungry...

...so he goes to look for something to eat. He wonders if they serve his favorite monster mash here. Perhaps this would be a good place for the monsters to meet.

Before he gets lost again...

FIND FRANKIE AT THE YUM-YUM EMPORIUM AND...

☐ Arrow
☐ Birdcage
☐ Bone
☐ Chicken man
☐ Cook
☐ Dogs (3)
☐ Fishing pole
☐ Football
☐ Knight
☐ Mailbox
☐ Manager
☐ Panda
☐ Pirate
☐ Princess
☐ Robot
☐ Rubber duck
☐ Salt shaker
☐ Scuba diver
☐ Sheriff
☐ Skulls (2)
☐ Space creature
☐ Star
☐ Straws (2)
☐ Sunglasses (2)
☐ Tombstone
☐ Tray of pizza
☐ Tuba
☐ Turtles (2)
☐ Volcano
☐ Wig

After lunch, Frankie wanders into the aquarium to see some underwater monsters. Even though they're all wet, they seem to be having a good time.

FIND FRANKIE IN THE AQUARIUM AND...

☐ Boat
☐ Bucket
☐ Cans of tuna
☐ Cat
☐ Diver
☐ Dog
☐ Duck
☐ Ear
☐ Eyeglasses
☐ Fisherman
☐ Flying fish
☐ Guitar
☐ Hammer
☐ Hearts (4)
☐ Ice skater
☐ Igloo
☐ Life preserver
☐ Mermaid
☐ Magnifying glass
☐ Merman
☐ Old-fashioned radio
☐ Sea horse
☐ Socks (2)
☐ Starfish (3)
☐ Stingray
☐ Submarine
☐ Surfer
☐ Swordfish (2)
☐ Tick-tack-toe
☐ Tiger
☐ Water leak
☐ Wooden leg

After watching the fish frolic, Frankie feels like having some fun too.

Hot dog! It's Frankie's first time on wheels! If only his monster friends could see him now.

FIND FRANKIE AT THE ROWDY ROLLER RINK AND...

- ☐ Apple
- ☐ Artist
- ☐ Basketball
- ☐ Bowling ball
- ☐ Boxer
- ☐ Boy Scout
- ☐ Cave man
- ☐ Centaur
- ☐ Centipede
- ☐ Convict
- ☐ Drum
- ☐ Fire hydrant
- ☐ Fish
- ☐ Ghost
- ☐ Giant roller skate
- ☐ Guitar
- ☐ Half-stop sign
- ☐ Hockey player
- ☐ Ice skater
- ☐ Jugglers (2)
- ☐ Paintbrushes (2)
- ☐ Piano
- ☐ Pillow
- ☐ Scarfs (2)
- ☐ Skier
- ☐ Snow woman
- ☐ Super hero
- ☐ Swan
- ☐ Three-legged skater
- ☐ Unicorn
- ☐ Weight lifter
- ☐ Witch
- ☐ Zebra

After rocking and rolling around the rink, Frankie sees a place with lots of space monsters on video screens. He hears bloops and bleeps, bzaps and bliks—sounds that Frankie's friends usually make.

FIND FRANKIE IN THE ARCADE AND...

- ☐ Angel
- ☐ Baseball
- ☐ Bat
- ☐ Bathtub
- ☐ Bomb
- ☐ Bottle
- ☐ Bow
- ☐ Carrot
- ☐ Darts (4)
- ☐ Dog
- ☐ Earmuffs
- ☐ Giraffe
- ☐ Hammer
- ☐ Headless player
- ☐ Heart
- ☐ Highest score
- ☐ Horseshoe
- ☐ Ice-cream cone
- ☐ Jack-o'-lantern
- ☐ Painter
- ☐ Paper airplane
- ☐ Pillow
- ☐ Pinocchio
- ☐ Rabbit
- ☐ Robot
- ☐ Snakes (5)
- ☐ Spinning top
- ☐ Surfer
- ☐ Traffic ticket
- ☐ Trash can
- ☐ Wrecking ball

All the noise makes Frankie want to look for a peaceful place...

...outside of the city. This seems like a great place to live. If only he can find a nice, ugly home where the monsters can meet.

FIND FRANKIE IN THE SUBURBS AND...

- ☐ Badminton game
- ☐ Bird
- ☐ Caddy
- ☐ Candle
- ☐ Clown
- ☐ Cow
- ☐ Dogs (3)
- ☐ Duck
- ☐ Fencing star
- ☐ Fire hydrants (4)
- ☐ Flat tire
- ☐ Footballs (2)
- ☐ Hearts (3)
- ☐ Hose
- ☐ Hot dog mobile
- ☐ Ice-cream cone
- ☐ Ice skate
- ☐ Kite
- ☐ Lion
- ☐ Marching band
- ☐ Paper delivery
- ☐ Photographer
- ☐ Pig
- ☐ Pyramid
- ☐ Shark
- ☐ Telescope
- ☐ Treasure chest
- ☐ Tepee
- ☐ Umbrella
- ☐ Unicorn
- ☐ Unicycle
- ☐ Zebra

Wait! Maybe there is a place! Can you see it?

There, at the top of the hill, Frankie finds the perfect meeting house. The monsters finally find Frankie and elect him President of the Monster Club. What a great time for a party!

FIND FRANKIE AT THE MONSTERS' NEW CLUBHOUSE AND...

- ☐ Bats (4)
- ☐ Bones (4)
- ☐ Bottle
- ☐ Candles (2)
- ☐ Clock
- ☐ Coffeepot
- ☐ Coffin
- ☐ Cup
- ☐ Dog
- ☐ Flower
- ☐ Flying carpet
- ☐ Football
- ☐ Ghosts (5)
- ☐ Happy star
- ☐ Headless man
- ☐ Light bulb
- ☐ Mail carrier
- ☐ Mouse
- ☐ Mummy
- ☐ Octopus
- ☐ Pencil sharpener
- ☐ Skulls (4)
- ☐ Sled
- ☐ Snake
- ☐ Sword
- ☐ Tick-tack-toe
- ☐ Tombstones (2)
- ☐ Thirteens (4)
- ☐ Three-headed monster
- ☐ Top hat
- ☐ TV set
- ☐ Two-headed monster
- ☐ Umbrella
- ☐ Witch

FIND FRANKIE   SEARCH FOR SUSIE   LOOK FOR LAURA   DETECT DONALD